DRAWINGS BY MALCOLM SPOONER

EVE MERRIAM

It Doesn't *Always* Have to Rhyme

ATHENEUM 1964 NEW YORK

for DAVID and STEVEN

POEMS

It Doesn't *Always*
Have to Rhyme

INSIDE A POEM

It doesn't always have to rhyme,
but there's the repeat of a beat, somewhere
an inner chime that makes you want to
tap your feet or swerve in a curve;
a lilt, a leap, a lightning-split:—
thunderstruck the consonants jut,
while the vowels open wide as waves in the noon-
    blue sea.

You hear with your heels, your eyes feel
what they never touched before:
fins on a bird, feathers on a deer;
taste all colors, inhale
memory and tomorrow and always the tang is
    today.

A SPELL OF WEATHER

Begone, calm.
Come, zephyr.
Blow, breeze.
All hail, hail, cloudburst, torrent.

Grow wind into gust, squall, williwaw;
Spout tempest, typhoon, gale,
Roar tornado;
Rip hurricane, rage tide!

Then spent,
Subside;
Beached. . . .

Skies clearing,
Cerulean,
Unrippled blue.

SPRING FEVER

Danny dawdles
Sally shilly-shallies
Lloyd loiters
Guy gambols
Sylvia saunters
Peter procrastinates
Amanda meanders
Leonard lingers
Samuel ambles
Dorothy dallies
Harry tarries
and Molly lolls.

WHO'S HERE?

Here's a curmudgeon.
What is he wearing?
He has a grudge on.

Is he down in the dumps?
Is he feeling low?
No.
He's in a high dudgeon.

HAVING WORDS

Did you ever take umbrage?

If you want to take umbrage
you don't have to shake
a bottle or open a jar.
Stay still where you are.
For it isn't like taking a pill,
or taking your leave,
or taking a walk,
or taking a chance or a fall;
or taking your time,
or taking time out,
or taking a turn about.
Nor is it like taking your share or your fill
of tea and cake or a malted milkshake.

It won't make you sick,
it won't keep you well.
Well, then, what on earth is it for?
And where can an umbrage be found to take?
In a store, in a zoo, in a lake?

Is it dotted or striped?
Is it round or oblong?
Does it fly into space?
Does it have *any* face?

Is it fierce, is it tame?
Of good or ill fame?
Can you give one to me or can it be bought?
In what college might umbrage be taught?
Is it for people or plants or ants
or strictly for the birds?
Is it down in the cellar or up on a shelf?

You'll have to find out for yourself
someday when you're having words.

DOUBLE TROUBLE

A scissor
and a trouser
were discussing their woes.

"Why," asked the scissor,
"do you suppose
one always has to make a pair?
It hardly seems fair
that there's never a chance to be one alone.
Always one has
to share
and *share*."

Said the trouser to the scissor,
"Yes, I acquiesce.
I'm agreed indeed!
For it's tiresome for me
to be perpetually
in a similar state of duality.
Can't I be a single pant
or a separate breech?
Instead of being half,
what joy to be an each!
Someday," said the trouser,
"I'll just let 'er rip!"

"Me, too," said the scissor,
"I'll just cut loose!"

"But alas," they both sighed, "what's the use?
Breaking out from a tandem team
is only for us a random dream.
Unless we could become reincarnated,
eternally we're fated mated to dwell:
one alone we're counted as merely residual,
having been created unindividual."

END OF WINTER

Bare-handed reach
to catch
April's
incoming curve.
      Leap
           higher than you thought you could
              and
Hold:
      Spring,
      Solid,
      Here.

MR. ZOO

He's a lion-hearted man,
He's a roadhog in his car,
He's a bear for work,
He can out-fox you by far.

He's sheepish, he's mousy,
He pussyfoots around;
He ferrets out secrets,
He's a sniffing newshound.

Sometimes he looks owlish,
He's dog-tired at night;
He weeps crocodile tears,
Has a wolfish appetite.

He turns gooseflesh when he's cold,
He's piggish as can be,
He's a muttonhead, he's hare-brained,
He's a mulish, busy bee.

He's bullheaded, cocksure,
Eagle-eyed and alas,
He's a catspaw, a loan-shark,
A snake in the grass.

His wife is a vixen,
She's a nag, she's a shrew;
She's a social butterfly
Who acts kittenish with you.

She's doe-eyed, she's slothful,
She crows a lot, too:
No wonder she's married
To a man like Mr. Zoo!

A VOTE FOR
VANILLA

Vanilla, vanilla, vanilla for me,
That's the flavor I savor particularly
In cake or ice cream
Or straight from the bean
In pudding, potatoes, in fish or in stew,
In a sundae, a Monday, the whole week-long
    through!

I care not a sou, a hoot, or scintilla,
A fig or a farthing—except for vanilla!
Boo, foo, eschew sarsaparilla;
More, adore, encore vanilla!
From the Antarctic to the Antilles,
Vive Vanilles!

On the first of Vanilla I'll write to you,
At half-past vanilla we'll rendezvous;
By the light of vanilla we'll dance and we'll fly
Until vanilla dawns in the sky.
Then to a vanilla villa we'll flee
By the vanilla side of the sea,
With vanilla tables, vanilla chairs,
Vanilla carpeting on the stairs,
Vanilla dogs, vanilla cats,
Vanilla shoes, vanilla hats,
Vanilla mice in vanilla holes,
Vanilla soup in vanilla bowls:

Vanilla, vaniller, vanillest for me,
The flavor I favor most moderately!

A COMMERCIAL FOR SPRING

Tired of slush and snow and sleet?
Then try this dandy calendar treat!

You'll like the longer, king-size days;
You, too, will sing this season's praise.

It's the scientific sunshine pill
(Without that bitter winter chill).

It's naturally warmer, it's toasted through,
Exclusively mild for you and *you.*

It comes in the handy three-month pack:
March, April, May—or your money back.

So ask for S-P-R-I-N-
G, you'll never regret it;
Remember the name, it's headed for fame:
Be the first on your block to get it!

A SHORT NOTE

In music
a hemidemisemiquaver is
a half
of a half
of a half
of an eighth of a note.

i.e.,
take note,
a 1/64th,
a fraction
whose action takes
the merest quiver of a sliver,
the fleetingest beat,
a flip, a zip, a lickety-split,
a snippet, a smidgeon,
a speck, a dot,
that's what
a hemidemisemiquaver is:
a splinter, a scratch, a pinprick, a nick of time,
a taxi-meter click going
flick, snick, hemidemisemiquaver quick!

ULULATION

With a bray, with a yap,
with a grunt, snort, neigh,
with a growl, bark, yelp,
with a buzz, hiss, howl,
with a chirrup, mew, moo,
with a snarl, baa, wail,
with a blatter, hoot, bay,
with a screech, drone, yowl,
with a cackle, gaggle, guggle,
with a chuck, cluck, clack,
with a hum, gobble, quack,
with a roar, blare, bellow,
with a yip, croak, crow,
with a whinny, caw, low,
with a bleat, with a cheep, with a squawk, with a
    squeak:

animals
        —and sometimes humans—
                        speak!

CITY TRAFFIC

Green as a seedling the one lane shines,
Red ripened blooms for the opposite lines;
Emerald shoot,
Vermilion fruit.

Now amber, now champagne, now honey: go slow:
Shift, settle, then gather and sow.

SOLITUDE

Solitude
is a mood to share
with the last day of autumn,
with the last leaf that falls,
with the last tree bare

and below is the root
the silent root

that will bear through the dark
through the cold
through the storm

that will bear
seed, bud and fruit
to the flowering air.

SERENDIPITY

If you are knightly on your daily way
to slay a dragon
and by that way
you spy a wagon
filled with jewels to the top-tippety,
that is serendipity.

Or if you are Adam adamantly out to do your duty,
and along your macadam route you encounter a
    beauty
who causes your heart to go flop-flippety,
that event is serendipity.
Sir, meet Lady Serendipity.

Wherever you search for thorns and turn up a
    rose,
there is that fortune you cannot importune:
there is where fair serendipity grows.

CHEERS

The frogs and the serpents each had a football
    team,
and I heard their cheer leaders in my dream:

"Bilgewater, bilgewater," called the frog,
"Bilgewater, bilgewater,
Sis, boom, bog!
Roll 'em off the log,
Slog 'em in the sog,
Swamp'em, swamp'em,
Muck mire quash!"

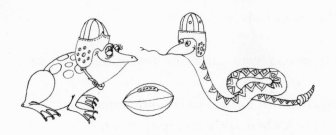

"Sisyphus, Sisyphus," hissed the snake,
"Sibilant, syllabub,
Syllable-loo-ba-lay.
Scylla and Charybdis,
Sumac, asphodel,
How do you spell Success?
With an S-S-S!"

A FISHY SQUARE DANCE

Tuna turn,
flounder round,
cuttlefish up,
halibut hold;

clam and salmon
trout about,
terrapin,
shrimp dip in;

forward swordfish,
mackerel back,
dace to the left,
ide to the right;

gallop scallop,
mussel perch,
grunnion run,
bass on down;

finnan haddie,
skate and fluke,
eel and sole,
shad and roe;

haddock, herring,
hake, squid, pike:
cod promenade
and lobster roll!

STARRY NIGHT I

Crescendo!
A million notes of music fly off the printed page
    in a melodic rage.
Brass, woodwinds, strings, percussion
all blare forth their orchestra of light
onto the nighttime stage.

STARRY NIGHT II

The night flowers for me.
As though the dew of every petal of every dawn
    has shaken free.
I swim in the skybloom sea.

METAPHOR

Morning is
a new sheet of paper
for you to write on.

Whatever you want to say,
all day,
until night
folds it up
and files it away.

The bright words and the dark words
are gone
until dawn
and a new day
to write on.

SIMILE: WILLOW AND GINKGO

The willow is like an etching,
Fine-lined against the sky.
The ginkgo is like a crude sketch,
Hardly worthy to be signed.

The willow's music is like a soprano,
Delicate and thin.
The ginkgo's tune is like a chorus
With everyone joining in.

The willow is sleek as a velvet-nosed calf;
The ginkgo is leathery as an old bull.
The willow's branches are like silken thread;
The ginkgo's like stubby rough wool.

The willow is like a nymph with streaming hair;
Wherever it grows, there is green and gold and
    fair.
The willow dips to the water,
Protected and precious, like the king's favorite
    daughter.

The ginkgo forces its way through gray concrete;
Like a city child, it grows up in the street.
Thrust against the metal sky,
Somehow it survives and even thrives.

My eyes feast upon the willow,
But my heart goes to the ginkgo.

Once, upon fair fortune's tree,
There grew a golden pear;
And as is fairly common there,
Wishes were granted three.

The first flung by
With a covetous eye:
> "Oh, that all alone I might
> For a quickening hour taste delight!"
> But single self could scarce begin,
> Could merely nibble the outer skin . . .

> *Who clutches at a lonely feast*
> *Must sour leave before the sweet*
> *for such is the gift of the golden pear*
> *such is the power of love to share.*

The second reined by
With a prudent eye:
  "I dearly long to bite deeper in,
   But juice might stain my spotless chin;
   I could only afford to enjoy it if
   I were neatly wearing a handkerchief..."

  Who waits for more inclining time
  will savor nothing of the feast
  for such is the gift of the golden pear
  such is the power of love to dare.

The third came by
With an eager eye:
  "Right ruddy in reach by the highway
    side,
   Fit for a king of the world and his bride—
   And who can that more certainly be
   Than the likes of all present company?"

  Consumed, and golden grew again.
  For he who most unsparing cares,
  the pear will never disappear
  the power of love is always here.

6.

You'll find, in French, that couplet's a little word
    for two;
Voici, how little time before our couplet's
    through.

5.

Of all the forms of verse that can be shown,
The couplet is the shortest one that's known.

4.

Rain raineth and sun sunneth;
Behold how my couplet runneth
    over.

3.

One and one is or are two?
I never know: do you?

2.

Want your meter
Even neater?

1.

Terse
Verse.

QUATRAIN

1.

Will it rain,
Or will it not rain?
Look again;
You've got a quatrain.

2.

You don't have to rhyme
Every line's last word;
You can leave out the first
And also the third.

LEANING ON A LIMERICK

1.

Let the limerick form be rehoised
In New Yorkish accents well voiced:
  "The thoid line is short,
  And so is the fourt',
While the fi't' and the second go foist."

2.

When a limerick line starts out first,
What follows is fated, accursed:
  If the third line takes tea,
  The fourth must agree,
While five, two, and one pool their thirst.

3.

Assiduously I'm attending
The limerick message I'm sending;
  I can get up to here,
  But alas and oh dear:
Now what do I do for an ending?

4.

You've a hunger to be newly-versed;
There are rhymes you would dare if you durst:
Macaroni, baloney,
Spumoni, tortoni—
But it's got to come out liverwurst.

ONE, TWO, THREE—GOUGH!

To make some bread you must have dough,
Isn't that sough?

If the sky is clear all through,
Is the color of it blough?

When is the time to put your hand to the plough?
Nough!

The handle on the pump near the trough
Nearly fell ough.

Bullies sound rough and tough enough,
But you can often call their blough.

GAZINTA

There's a strange sort of bird of a word
That abides near the Great Divide;
A gazinta is this bird absurd.

And here is how it got its name:
Two gazinta four two times,
And four gazinta eight the same.

SOME USES FOR POETRY

to paint without a palette
to dance without music
to speak without speaking

to feel the strangeness between hot and cold
to feel the likeness of hot and cold
to plunge into both at the same moment

BEWARE OF THE DOGGEREL

A Whippet
will sip at
Pekoe teas;

a Pekingese
prefers Limburger cheese;

an Afghan
will eat a half-can
of peas;

for a Scottie
if it's hot e-
nough, a curry; for

a Terrier
a berry or
very ripe cherry;

any bite in a lunch-box found
suits the appetite of a Foxhound;

mealy ham
for a Sealyham;

while the chow for a Chow
is chow-chow. Bow-wow!

OZ.

Whoever discounts
the ounce
as one of the smallest amounts
has never met up with the ounce
that belongs to the cat family.

This jungle ounce
will jounce
you out of complacency.
If you try to trounce
this ounce,
you will be chastened hastily;
for this ounce
does more than flounce;
this ounce can bounce,
this ounce can *pounce*.

So if you meet up with an ounce,
announce yourself as a friend,
or it might be The End.

P.S. Better not take a chounce.

DITTO MARKS or,
HOW DO YOU AMUSE A MUSE?

How do you amuse
     " "
when intent
     " "   she skulks,
wearing a furbelow
with   " " " ?

If she's sulky often
at quarter   " " ,
roll out the red carpet
and give her a " " ;
if still she's stand-offish,
try platters   " "

THE EGOTISTICAL ORCHESTRA

Vaunts violoncello,
"I'm a fine fellow."

Boasts bass,
"I'm the ace."

Flaunts French horn,
"*Sans moi*, all's forlorn."

Pipes flute,
"I'm some sweet toot."

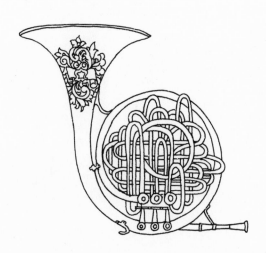

Brags piano, "I'm both upright *and*
grand."

Snoots cymbal, "My crashing
is simply smashing."

Vies xylophone,
"I set a high tone."

Raps baton, "Come on,
knock off the cacophony,
get Bach to Tschaikovsky,
I'll call the tune."

TITTLE AND JOT, JOT AND TITTLE

If you add a tittle
to a jot,
you still will not
have a lot,
since a tittle's just a bit,
and a jot is but a little.

Jot on top of tittle,
tittle over jot,
either way around,
it matters not.
Jot plus tittle,
tittle plus jot,
add the job lot
and what have you got?
Not a whole lot.
Still just a bit.
For tittle and jot, jot and tittle,
their allotted lot is to be little.

ONOMATOPOEIA and
ONOMATOPOEIA II

The rusty spigot
sputters,
utters
a splutter,
spatters a smattering of drops,
gashes wider;
slash,
splatters,
scatters,
spurts,
finally stops sputtering
and plash!
gushes rushes splashes
clear water dashes.

Therus
ty spi
     gots
        put
tersut
ters a splu
t
terspat   ters a smat   teringof
drop
    s
g'a s h e s w i d e r
s
 l
  a
   s
    h
spl tt
  a ers
sc   er
  a t t
  u t   s
  p r s
s   fi
nally stops stut
ter
ing
and plash gushesrushessplashes
CLEAR WATER DASHES.

A CLICHÉ

is what we all say
when we're too lazy
to find another way

and so we say

warm as toast,
quiet as a mouse,
slow as molasses,
quick as a wink.

Think.
Is toast the warmest thing you know?
Think again, it might not be so.
Think again: it might even be snow!
Soft as lamb's wool, fleecy snow,
a lacy shawl of new-fallen snow.

Listen to that mouse go
scuttling and clawing,
nibbling and pawing.
A mouse can speak
if only a squeak.

Is a mouse the quietest thing you know?
Think again, it might not be so.
Think again: it might be a shadow.
Quiet as a shadow,
quiet as growing grass,
quiet as a pillow,
or a looking glass.

Slow as molasses,
quick as a wink.
Before you say so,
take time to think.

Slow as time passes
when you're sad and alone;
quick as an hour can go
happily on your own.

1.

What is a *llano?*
Is it a hill? Ah no,
It's plain as can be
And grassy.

2.

If the aardvark
haad aa caar
aand went out aafter daark,
he might find it haard
to paark.

BEWARE, or
BE YOURSELF

Don't begrudge,
don't beseech,
don't besot,
don't besmirch,
don't belabor,
don't belittle,
don't befuddle,
don't befog,
don't benight,
don't belay,
don't bedizen,
don't bedeck,
don't beguile,
don't bewitch,
don't behead,
just behave!

WHAT DID YOU SAY?

A poem rarely has to shout,
for even when it is addressing a crowd

it is speaking only to you,
to you.

So when the syllables repeat,
it is sheerly for the music,
clearly.

NYM AND GRAPH

A sound-alike
Is a homonym:
Sing a *hymn,*
Look at *him.*

A spell-alike
Is a homograph:
A general *staff,*
A walking *staff.*

Said Homograph to Homonym,
"Although I don't mean to be mean,
You cannot do the things I do."

Said Homonym to Homograph,
"What great scene have you ever seen?"

Said Homograph, "From my point of view
I once saw a saw saw and then a sink sink,
I saw a fly fly and a rose that rose up,
I sat down upon down,
I felt a felt hat,
And met a fair maiden at the fair;
And that's fair enough. Now I dare *you* to tell!"

"Well," said Homonym, "it's true
I can't do what you can do,
And furthermore I don't want to . . .
For I had four cents for fare for the fair,
But it didn't make sense to go in where
I'd wear a tie that was not in a knot,
So instead I watched blue smoke that blew,
And then flew straightway up the flue.
Now tell me, Homograph, can *you*
See things from *my* point of view?
For I, sir, ay yes, I eye a dear deer,
And a hare with hair that is half of a pair
While I pare a pear beside a new gnu
And shoo a bare bear away from my shoe—
And all this I do at ten to two, too!"

A JAMBOREE FOR J

It's hard to make a *j*
sound anything but joyful:
it's jubilant, it's jocund,
it joins in a jig.
It japes, it jibes, it jingles,
it jitterbugs, it jets.
It jangles, it jumps rope,
it jounces in a jeep.
It jiggles, it joggles,
it's juicy, it's jamful,
it's a jester, a jockey,
a jaunty jackanapes.
It's a juggler, a jouster,
a jar full of jellybeans,
it's a julep, a jujube,
a jocose jinni,
a journey in a jolly boat—

by jeepers, by jiminy,
by Juno and by Jupiter,
what jovial high jinks!

UNFINISHED KNEWS ITEM

A well-known knavish knight with knobby knees
had a knack of knotting his knapsack
while he knelt in his knickerbockers.
One day he knocked his knuckles with a knife,
but knobody knoticed what happened knext. . . .

BE MY NON-VALENTINE

I have searched my Thesaurus through
to find a synonym for you;
here are some choice words that may do:

you're a hoddy-doddy, a dizzard, a ninny, a dolt,
a booby, a looby, a fribble, a gowk,
a nonny, a nizy, a nincompoop,
a churl, a scrimp, a knag, a trapes,
a lubber, a marplot, an oaf, a droil,
a mopus, a flat, a muff, a doit,
a mugwump, a dimwit, a flunkey, a swab,
a bane, a murrain, a malkin, a pox,
a sloven, a slammerkin, a draggel tail,
frumpery, scrannel, and kickshaw, too!

MNEMONIC FOR SPELUNKING

From the cavern of my mind
Here's a remembrance clue
That was passed along to me,
Now I pass it on to you:

Stalactites from the ceiling show;
Stalagmites from the ground up grow.

MONA LISA

"You'll mean what I say," tells prose.

"Say what I mean," smiles the poem.

> *If you can, if you can.*
> *Catch me if you can.*
> *If you can catch yourself, you can.*

THUMBPRINT

In the heel of my thumb
are whorls, whirls, wheels
in a unique design:
mine alone.
What a treasure to own!
My own flesh, my own feelings.
No other, however grand or base,
can ever contain the same.
My signature,
thumbing the pages of my time.
My universe key,
my singularity.
Impress, implant,
I am myself,
of all my atom parts I am the sum.
And out of my blood and my brain
I make my own interior weather,
my own sun and rain.
Imprint my mark upon the world,
whatever I shall become.

SKYWRITING

1.
Fireworks!
They shower down as verbs,
and come to rest as nouns.

Fountain in reverse,
words that delight take flight,
flash like fireworks in the air,
blazon and remain there.

2.
Adjectives like leaves
palpitate the trees.
Yearly the seasons must renew
as April's green and singing sound
falls to silent winter ground.

A poem shapes the landscape,
holds the singing green.
Leaves that do not die,
planted in the poem sky.

3.
Birds write verses in the sky;
swift verbs that fly,
slow nouns in their downy nest.

Wingbeat repeat, repeat
the symmetry of birds, of words.

The flight soaring,
the song outpouring.
The flight dying,
the song still flying.

METHUSELAH

Methuselah, Methuselah,
So long-lived a man was he,
The candles on his birthday cake
Lit all the ships at sea!

Methuselah, that longevity man,
Had a long, *long,* LONG white beard
That started to grow in Canada
And in Florida still appeared!

Methuselah, that high old-timer,
Never was one for tears;
He thought the world was a funny place—
And laughed for a thousand years!

That millennium man might be living yet,
And he'd write this instead of me,
Except that one day he kicked up his heels
And rocked himself with glee;

For it struck him as the funniest sight
That people on earth were so queer:
With only two legs and only two arms
And only two ears to hear,

With less than three eyes in each single head,
It was strange as strange could be;
They all looked so very much alike
In the human family

You could scarcely tell one from another
Compared to outer-space faces,
And their world was so small compared to all
Interplanetary places,

And yet they fought among themselves:
Imagine such idiocy?
That antic antique laughed himself sick
And died of hilarity.

WHY I DID NOT REIGN

I longed to win the spelling bee
And remembered the rule
I had learned in school:

"I before E,
Except after C."

Friend, believe me,
No one was going to deceive me.

Fiercely I practiced, the scepter I'd wield,
All others their shields in the field would yield!

Alas, before my very eyes
A weird neighbor in a beige veil
Feigning great height and weighty size
Seized the reins and ran off with the prize.

Now I no longer deign to remember that rule.
Neither
Any other either.

CONVERSATION WITH MYSELF

This face in the mirror
stares at me
demanding *Who are you? What will you become?*
and taunting, *You don't even know.*
Chastened, I cringe and agree
and then
because I'm still young,
I stick out my tongue.

FIRST DAY OF SUMMER

Dive into grass
body my bathysphere
taking me past green
      blue-black
          to blinding white below
then up through midnight
kick clear, shake free and run to
overtake the sun
mount that burning snowy peak
eat my fill of cherries
then slide down the sky
flinging the pits at stars I pass by
bull's-eye

VACATION

I am Paul Bunyan,
the sun is my bounding ball.

Leonardo,
the sun is my slapping brush.

Bronco-buster,
the sun my digging heels.

Sky is my apple,
I bite into blue.

A snorting whale,
I blow out blue.

Sky is my knife,
I cut through blue.

The day is my dog,
lapping, running.

The day is my boat,
lolling, lazy.

Day is my rope,
twirling, turning.

The world is my hat
bowing from hair.

The world is my belt
warm at my waist.

The world is my key
private in pocket.

Turn key in the door
and enter once more:

I am Paul Bunyan,
the sun is my ball . . .

FOREVER

My father tells me
that when he was a boy
he once crashed a ball
through a neighbor's window.

He does not mean to,
but he lies.

I know that aeons ago
the world was ice
and mud
and fish climbed out of the sea
to reptiles on land
to dinosaurs and mammals;

and I know also
that archeologists have found
remains of ancient times
when men lived in caves
and worshiped weather.

Nonetheless I know
that my father,
a grown man,
coming home at night
with work-lines in his face
and love for me hidden behind
the newspaper in his hand,
has always been so
since the world began.

COLOR

What is the difference
Between man and man?

White as chalk,
White as snow,
Black as night,
Black as coal;

But people are pink
Or brown or tan
Or yellow-brown-pink
Or pinkish-brown-tan.

Not much difference, I think,
Between man and man.

LEAVETAKING

Vacation is over;
It's time to depart.
I must leave behind
 (although it breaks my heart)

Tadpoles in the pond,
A can of eels,
A leaky rowboat,
Abandoned car wheels;

For I'm packing only
Necessities:
A month of sunsets
And two apple trees.

THE TIME IS:

Do you know the hour when all opposites meet
in the blaze of up and the haze of down?

In the fire of yes and the ice of no?

In the oil of rain and the drybone wind?

In leafy will and bare branch won't?

Do you know the hour?
It is always now.

HOW TO EAT A POEM

Don't be polite.
Bite in.
Pick it up with your fingers and lick the juice that
     may run down your chin.
It is ready and ripe now, whenever you are.

You do not need a knife or fork or spoon
or plate or napkin or tablecloth.

For there is no core
or stem
or rind
or pit
or seed
or skin
to throw away.

ADVERTISEMENT
FOR A DIVERTISSEMENT

It's never too early,
it's never too late;
it's always the right time
to celebrate
any old thing and everything,
a jump or a season or a mattress spring,
something quotidian,
something obsidian,
an apogee, a perigee,
a jigamaree, a filigree,
an ibex, an apex, a portmanteau,
a charivari, a persiflage,
a quodlibet, a brouhaha,
a gaggle, a gluggle, a glockenspiel,
a googol, a glottal-*stop*.

The weather is fine,
be it sun, albeit rain;
it's always the right time
to entertain
a cavil, a quibble,
a notion, a motion,
a trivet, a tippet,
a cravat, a gallus,
a quip or a frippery.

Cavort, gallivant,
escort, disport
a howdah, a nadir, a hippodrome,
an equine, a nightmare, a bridle, a grooming,
a paradox, a paradigm,
an it, a her, a they, a him,
a mishmash, a mincemeat, a gallimaufry,
a purple cow, an anyhow,
something outrageous, something indigenous,
something upholstered, something downtown,
a frontispiece, a bacchanal,
an oddity, eventually
a nonesuch, a quidnunc,
essentially
the quiddity of you and me.

"I," SAYS THE POEM

"I," says the poem arrogantly,
"I am a cloud,
I am a tree.

I am a city,
I am the sea,
I am a golden
Mystery."

How can it be?

A poem is written
by some someone,
someone like you,
or someone like me

who blows his nose,
who breaks shoelaces,
who hates and loves,
who loses gloves,
who eats, who weeps,
who laughs, who sleeps,

an ordinary he or she
extraordinary as you or me

whose thoughts stretch high
as clouds in the sky,

whose memories
root deep as trees,

whose feelings choke
like city smoke,

whose fears and joys in waves redound
like the ocean's tidal sound,

who daily solves a mystery:
each hour is new, what will it be?

"I," says the poem matter-of-factly,
"I am a cloud,
I am a tree.

I am a city,
I am the sea,

I am a golden
Mystery."

But, adds the poem silently,
I cannot speak until you come.
Reader, come, come with me.

EVE MERRIAM

It Doesn't Always Have to Rhyme, like *There Is No Rhyme for Silver,* grew out of Eve Merriam's conviction that there should be poetry for young people that is fun and yet memorable and in a modern vein. These books have been written with the same care and out of the same depth as her numerous books of adult poetry. Among these, *Family Circle,* her first book, was awarded the Yale Series of Younger Poets Prize and was published with an introduction by Archibald MacLeish.

At one time Miss Merriam conducted a weekly radio series on modern poetry for radio station WQXR in New York and wrote a daily verse column for the newspaper *PM.* She has also published fiction and nonfiction in many magazines and anthologies. These pieces have been widely reprinted.

Although her collections of poetry for children number only two, she has done a number of picture books for children, including *A Gaggle of Geese* and *Mommies at Work.*